To the reader:

Welcome to the DK ELT Graded Readers! These readers are different. They explore aspects of the world around us: its history, geography, science … and a lot of other things. And they show the different ways in which people live now, and lived in the past.

These DK ELT Graded Readers give you material for reading for information, and reading for pleasure. You are using your English to do something real. The illustrations will help you understand the text, and also help bring the Reader to life. There is a glossary to help you understand the special words for this topic. Listen to the cassette or CD as well, and you can really enter the world of the Olympic Games, the *Titanic*, or the Trojan War … and a lot more. Choose the topics that interest you, improve your English, and learn something … all at the same time.

Enjoy the series!

To the teacher:

This series provides varied reading practice at five levels of language difficulty, from elementary to FCE level:

BEGINNER
ELEMENTARY A
ELEMENTARY B
INTERMEDIATE
UPPER INTERMEDIATE

The language syllabus has been designed to suit the factual nature of the series, and includes a wider vocabulary range than is usual with ELT readers: language linked with the specific theme of each book is included and glossed. The language scheme, and ideas for exploiting the material (including the recorded material) both in and out of class are contained in the Teacher's Resource Book. We hope you and your students enjoy using this series.

Dorling **DK** Kindersley

LONDON, NEW YORK, SYDNEY, DELHI,
PARIS, MUNICH & JOHANNESBURG

Originally published as Eyewitness Reader
Plants Bite Back! in 1999 and adapted as an
ELT Graded Reader for
Dorling Kindersley by

studio cactus ○

13 SOUTHGATE STREET WINCHESTER HAMPSHIRE SO23 9DZ

Published in Great Britain by
Dorling Kindersley Limited
9 Henrietta Street, London WC2E 8PS

2 4 6 8 10 9 7 5 3 1

Copyright © 2000
Dorling Kindersley Limited, London

A CIP catalogue record for this book is
available from the British Library.

ISBN 0-7513-2925-8

Colour reproduction by Colourscan, Singapore
Printed and bound in China by
L. Rex Printing Co., Ltd
Text film output by Chimera TRT, UK

The publisher would like to thank the following
for their kind permission to reproduce their photographs:
c=centre; t=top; b=below; l=left; r=right

Heather Angel: 10 l, 13 t, 19 t; **Ardea London Ltd:** John Mason 25 r,
Y. Arthus-Bertrand 44 cl; **Biofotos:** Paul Simons 14 cl; **Bridgeman Art
Library, London / New York:** 40 bc; **Bruce Coleman Ltd:** John
Cancalosi 39, Kim Taylor 11, Leonard Lee Rue 43 tc; **Ronald Grant
Archive:** 13 br; **N.H.P.A:** G.I. Bernard 12 crb, George Gainsburgh
12 cra; **Oxford Scientific Films:** Peter Parks 12 cr; Photos
Horticultural: 41 clb; **Planet Earth Pictures:** Frank Krahmer 42 br;
Royal Horticultural Society: 33; **Science Photo Library:** David
Nunuk 18 tr, Dr P. Marazzi 24 cl, Sue Ford 47 t

See our complete catalogue at
www.dk.com

Contents

ELT Graded Readers

ELEMENTARY B

DANGEROUS PLANTS

Written by
Sarah Woolard

Series Editor Susan Holden

A Dorling Kindersley Book

The World of Plants

Plants are everywhere. You can find them growing all over the world. This is a good thing for us, because if we didn't have plants, we would not survive. There would be no life on earth as we know it. Why are plants so important? There are many reasons, but one of their most important jobs is to give food. Plants provide food for animals and people.

But not all plants provide food. Some of them are dangerous to eat. These plants have developed special ways to stop animals or people eating them. One of these ways is to make poison (something that makes you ill or kills you if you eat it) which often tastes horrible and keeps the animals away.

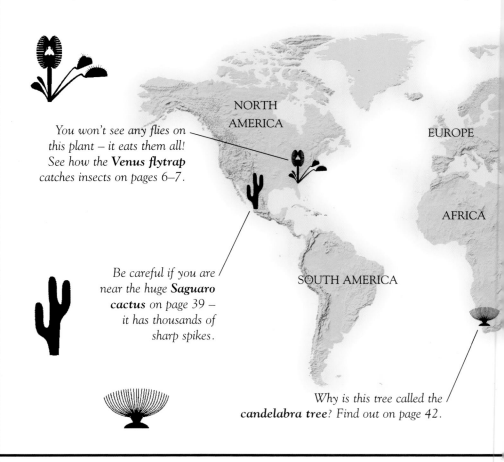

*You won't see any flies on this plant – it eats them all! See how the **Venus flytrap** catches insects on pages 6–7.*

NORTH AMERICA

EUROPE

AFRICA

*Be careful if you are near the huge **Saguaro cactus** on page 39 – it has thousands of sharp spikes.*

SOUTH AMERICA

*Why is this tree called the **candelabra tree**? Find out on page 42.*

Another way to keep animals away is to grow spikes. The spikes are like sharp needles, and hurt any animal that comes near. Some plants have stings (like a wasp). When you touch them, your skin turns red and itches or gets hot. Animals soon learn not to go near these kinds of plants. But some plants are even better at stopping animals. Usually the animals eat the plants, but these plants catch the animals and eat THEM!

You can find these strange (and sometimes dangerous) plants in every country in the world – plants that can sting, scratch, and bite animals and people. Do you know of any strange or dangerous plants in your country? The map below shows where some of them grow around the world – and where you can read more about them in this book.

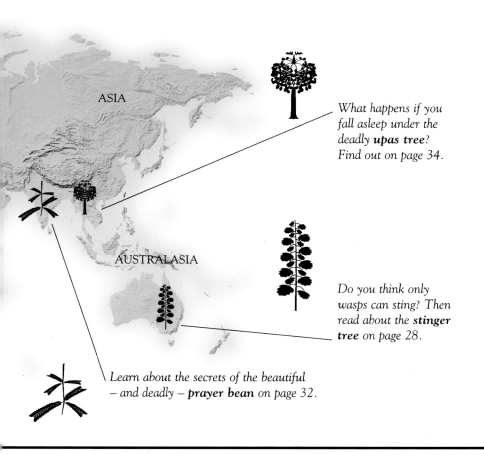

ASIA

AUSTRALASIA

*What happens if you fall asleep under the deadly **upas tree**? Find out on page 34.*

*Do you think only wasps can sting? Then read about the **stinger tree** on page 28.*

*Learn about the secrets of the beautiful – and deadly – **prayer bean** on page 32.*

Greedy Green Eaters

At the side of the water, a beautiful, blue damselfly is moving around. It flies over the flowers and grasses, and then sees an interesting plant with strange leaves. The damselfly hovers (*flies without moving*) above the plant and looks more closely, then it lands on the leaves. It is a big mistake. SNAP! The leaves close together and catch the damselfly. The sides of the leaves are like a comb, and they lock together very tightly. The fly is trapped and can't move. Soon it will be dead.

The name of the plant is the Venus flytrap, and it is one example of a carnivorous plant – in other words a plant that eats meat. These meat-eating plants are quite unusual, and are a very interesting group to study.

There are about 250,000 different kinds of plants in the world, but only a small number of these (about 400) are carnivorous, like the Venus flytrap in the picture here. But why did plants start eating meat? Many animals are carnivorous ... surely plants only eat meat in horror movies!

Carnivorous plants grow in wet areas, where the ground is very soft – these areas are called bogs, marshes, or swamps. The ground in these places is not very good for plants to grow. There aren't enough minerals in the ground to provide food for the plants. So the plants get extra minerals from insects – and they have learnt how to catch them and eat them to survive. They have learnt how to be hunters.

It is possible for these carnivorous plants to live without eating insects, but the extra minerals help them to grow better and stronger.

The Venus flytrap grows on the marshes in North and South Carolina in the USA.

When you read about a plant like this eating an insect, it all looks very simple. But it is not very easy for a plant to catch an insect. The Venus flytrap can't move around, and it has no eyes to see the flies above or beside it. It can't hear the noise of insects coming near. So how does it catch something in its leaves – especially something that can move fast, like a fly?

The plant doesn't have to move, it just waits for the meal to come to it. Like all traps, the Venus flytrap uses a special bait. This means it has something that will attract or invite the insects to come near. The Venus flytrap has a very sweet, sugary liquid on its leaves. The insects can smell this, and they think it is delicious – this is the bait. The sweet liquid smells like a tasty meal, so the insects fly nearer and land on the leaves. Of course, they are right – it is a tasty meal, but the delicious meal is them!

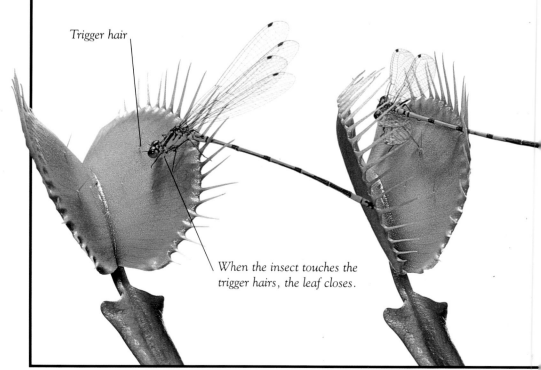

Trigger hair

When the insect touches the trigger hairs, the leaf closes.

The plant has to work very fast to catch the insect, so when the insect lands on the leaves, the trap starts to work immediately. There are three very small hairs on each leaf, and these are like tiny triggers. As soon as the insect touches these hairs, the trap closes, like the teeth in a mouth. And this happens very quickly. In less than a second, the sides of the leaves close, and the insect can't get out. This is enough to trap a large insect like the damselfly. Now the Venus flytrap has caught its dinner – but it takes a long time to eat it.

The leaves slowly move closer and closer together, and after about half an hour, they are shut tight. Now the leaves are like a cup, and it fills with a special liquid. In fact it is more like a stomach, and over the next week or two the body of the insect dissolves (*becomes liquid*) inside this "stomach". Now the plant has a cup of "insect soup"! The Venus flytrap can drink this liquid soup through its leaves, and in this way it takes in extra vitamins to help it grow.

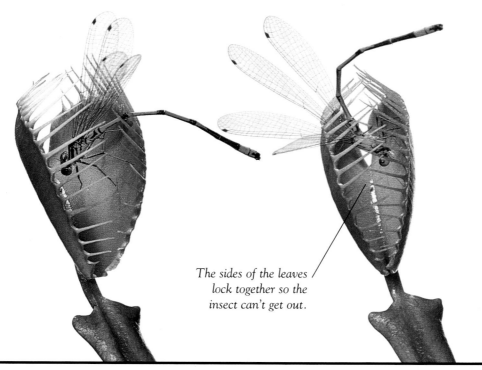

The sides of the leaves lock together so the insect can't get out.

The Venus flytrap is the only plant with a killer mouth like this, but other plants have different ways to catch their prey (*the food they kill*). For example, the bladderwort has a very clever way of catching lunch – it sucks up its food like a vacuum cleaner sucks up dust.

These plants are found in many different countries, and can grow wherever it is wet. A bladderwort eats very small water insects and fish. It can eat some baby fish (called fry) in one bite. Bladderworts can grow in very wet ground, but they are not like most other plants we see. Usually, they float around on the top of the water in ponds or lakes. You can find them in water everywhere – even in the small pools of rainwater among the leaves of other plants. The bladderwort is one of the most successful carnivorous plants. Most carnivorous plants can take in food from the ground through their roots, so the insects they eat give them extra food. But the bladderwort can catch all the food it needs in the water, from the insects and other small creatures living there. This means that the bladderwort doesn't need to have any roots in the ground to find food – and so, unlike most plants, it can move or float around in the water. This is a plant that chases its food.

The flowers and the stem of the bladderwort grow above the water.

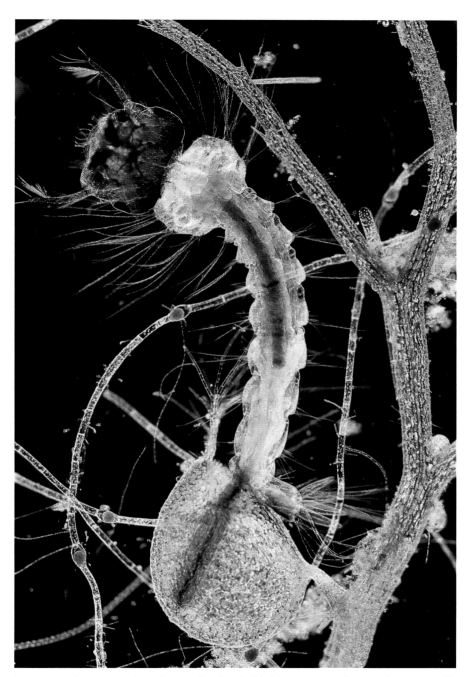

This insect (a mosquito larva) is too big for the bladderwort to suck up and eat – it will probably get away.

Unlike the Venus flytrap, it isn't easy to see the bladderwort catch its prey – it is very small and you need to use a microscope. The plant has many long, thin, green roots. All along these roots there are small, round traps that look like tiny bubbles. Usually, these bubbles have no strong colour – you can see through them. After the bladderwort catches its prey, the bubbles change colour to black.

How does the trap work? Each bubble has a little door that can shut tight. To make the trap ready, the plant sucks the water out of the bubble, and the walls of the bubble close in (like a balloon with no air). There are very small trigger hairs on the trap, like the hairs on a Venus flytrap. When an insect (like the water flea in the pictures here) touches the hairs, the trap door suddenly opens. This makes the walls of the bubble explode. Because there is no air inside the bubble, water is sucked in quickly, taking the flea with it. This makes the plant like a vacuum cleaner – it sucks the flea or other insect inside it. This is a very efficient way of eating food.

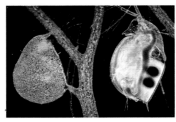

A water flea gets too close to a bladderwort.

The flea is sucked into the trap.

The bladderwort eats its meal.

The roots of a bladderwort, showing the small traps like bubbles.

SNAP! The door closes again and the insect is trapped inside. This happens very quickly, in about one-fiftieth of a second, and much faster than the eye can see.

Then the plant starts to suck the air out of the bubble again. It fills the bubble with a special liquid, and (like the Venus flytrap) this liquid kills and dissolves the body of the insect. Now the plant is ready to eat, and it can drink the "insect soup" slowly. After about two hours, the bladderwort is ready to set its trap again – just one of the many small traps along its roots, all working at the same time.

Plants that eat people!
Carnivorous plants usually eat insects. People-eating plants, like this one from the film *Little Shop of Horrors*, exist only in stories and films.

The bladderwort can move around, and its special
bubbles have doors that open and close – this
makes it easier to catch its prey. The Venus
flytrap can open and close its leaves to
trap insects. But pitcher plants can't
move around, and they have no special
"doors" or moving parts. They have a different way of
catching their prey. These plants drown their prey in pools of
liquid. The liquid is a mixture of water and special juices that
dissolves the bodies of insects.

The plant keeps this killer liquid in special leaves that
look like jugs (called pitchers). There are many different kinds
of pitcher plants, with different shapes and sizes of leaves, and
some examples are shown in the pictures here. Some are long
and thin, others are round or fat.

The biggest pitcher plants
grow in Borneo, an island in
Southeast Asia. These huge
pitchers can hold 2–4 litres of
liquid, and they sit on the
ground. They are big enough to
trap insects and small birds, and
they can even catch small
animals like rats!

But the plants are not
always killers. The monkey cup
pitcher plant, for example, gets
its name because thirsty monkeys
come to drink from its pitchers.
The pitchers are strong, and they can be very useful in
everyday life. People in some countries use them to carry
water to their homes, and others use them as cooking pots.

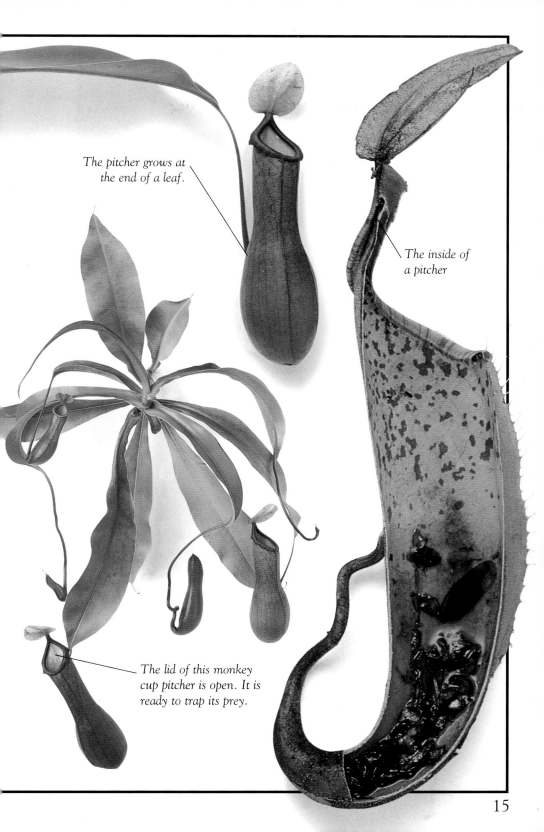

The pitcher grows at
the end of a leaf.

The inside of
a pitcher

The lid of this monkey
cup pitcher is open. It is
ready to trap its prey.

But if a pitcher plant has no moving parts, how does it catch its prey? It has a very simple, but very clever way of trapping food. When an insect is flying through the jungle, there are many different flowers and plants around it. But it is always easy to see the brightly coloured pitcher among the other plants. The bright colours and strange shapes of the pitchers attract insects.

First, the insect lands on the top of the pitcher, and looks more closely. It can smell the sweet liquid around the ends of the plant, and it can see the clear path going down into the delicious liquid in the pitcher. Of course, the hungry insect does not stop for long. It goes down inside the pitcher to drink the sweet-smelling liquid.

But walking along the leaf inside the pitcher is very difficult, and soon the insect can't walk. Small parts of the leaf fall off, and the insect's feet move in different directions as it starts to slip. The insect slips around on the inside of the leaf, and every time it moves, it slips more. Walking gets more and more difficult. Finally the insect can't keep standing on its legs on the leaf and it starts to fall. SPLASH! It falls into the sweet liquid in the pitcher. There is no way out now – the insect goes down into the liquid and drowns. The body of the insect will dissolve in the liquid, and soon the pitcher plant can start to eat its meal. Like the Venus flytrap and the bladderwort, it can enjoy an "insect soup". And because some pitcher plants are very big, there may be many different insects trapped in the deadly "soup" at the same time.

Special parts of the plant inside the pitcher make a liquid that can dissolve the bodies of insects.

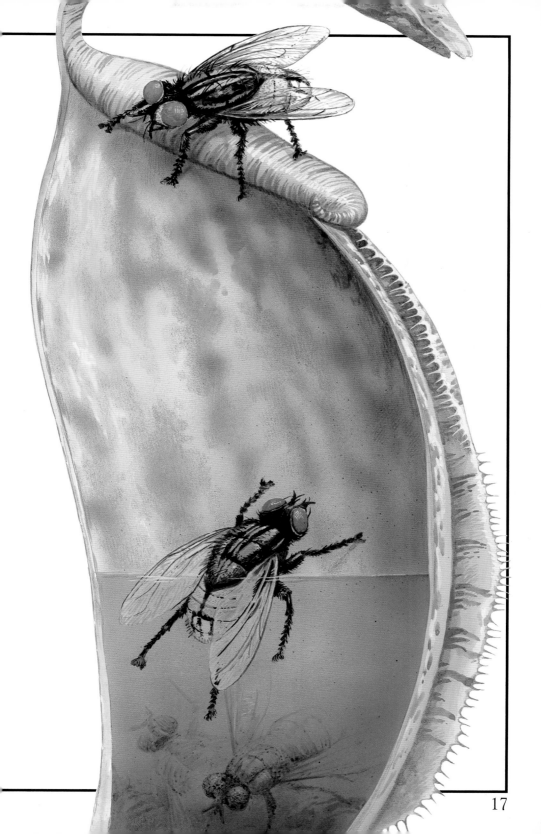

Another plant with a clever way of catching insects is called the sundew plant. This plant has a bright, sticky liquid all over its leaves – and this attracts insects to their death. The sundew doesn't sit still like the pitcher plant – it has a much more active kind of trap.

The name of the plant comes from its leaves. When the sun shines on them, these leaves reflect the light. This is because they have small drops of liquid on them. They look like small drops of water on the grass in the early morning (called dew). The shiny drops on the leaves look like a delicious drink, and this attracts the insects. But it may be a big mistake! Sometimes the most beautiful things in nature are also the most dangerous.

A group of sundew plants growing in the wet ground.

Sundews grow in wet ground, where usually it is difficult for plants to survive. You can find them in Africa and all over Europe, in wet bogs and marshes (like the bladderwort). But most of these plants grow in the west of Australia, and there you can find them in dry areas as well as in wet lands. There are many different kinds of sundew plants around the world. The smallest is only a few centimetres long, but some kinds of sundew grow into sticky bushes (like small trees) almost a metre high.

There are hundreds of tiny hairs all over the leaves of the sundew plant, and the hairs on the outside are about a centimetre long. These hairs are more dangerous than they look! Each hair has a small drop of sticky liquid (like glue) on the end. There is no sweet smell here, but the leaves look good to eat. The insects see the sunlight on the liquid, but they do not see the hairs.

As soon as an insect comes near and lands on one of the leaves, it touches one of the hairs. The sticky liquid catches and holds the insect, and it can't move away. When the insect tries to move and fly away, it touches another hair … then another. It is trapped.

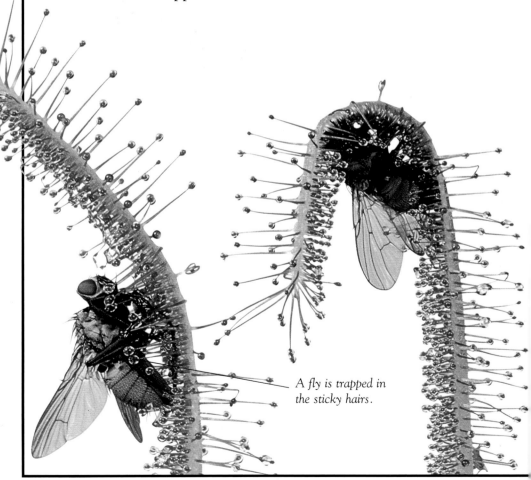

A fly is trapped in the sticky hairs.

Why buy flypaper?
In some countries, people put up special sticky paper to catch flies. But in other parts of the world, like Portugal, people sometimes put up sundew plants, and the flies stick to the plants.

The hairs that the insect touches help to trap it, and the more it moves, the more it sticks. But the sundew plant has other surprises, because the hairs near the trapped insect also start to move. These hairs also stick to the insect and hold it. In the end the insect can't move, and it dies. If the insect is a big one, and it is trapped near the outside of the plant, then the hairs can move it. They can pass the insect along to the centre of the plant. The liquid in the drops catches the insect, and also dissolves its body. Then the hairs can drink the liquid, taking the food into the plant.

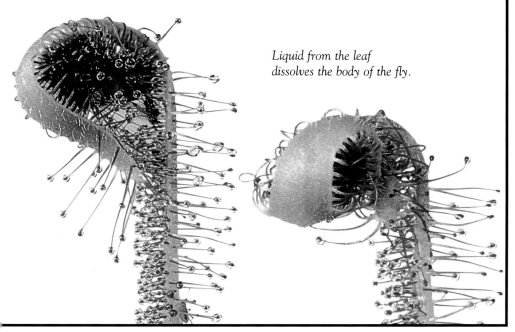

Liquid from the leaf dissolves the body of the fly.

Deadly Weeds

We know that some plants catch and eat insects and animals. But what about humans? Carnivorous plants are not dangerous for humans, but some other plants are a big problem. In the picture below you can see a normal area of woodland in North America. People go for a walk in places like this every day. It looks very nice and relaxing. But do you know which plants are safe, and which are dangerous?

Some plants make a poison to help them survive. This poison doesn't kill, but it stops animals from eating the plants.

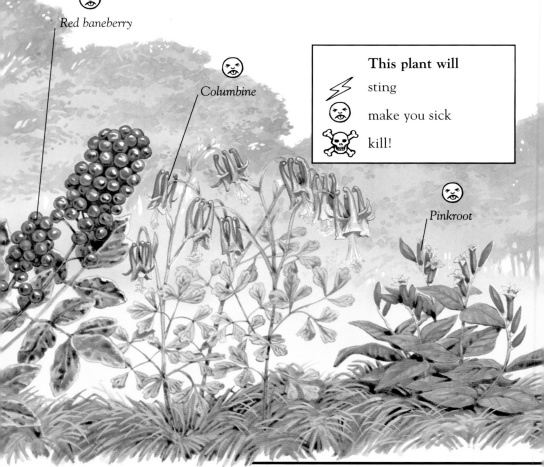

Red baneberry

Columbine

This plant will

⚡ sting

😖 make you sick

☠ kill!

Pinkroot

If you touched one of these plants, it could sting you. This means you get a painful, itchy feeling on your skin – and sometimes your skin turns red with small spots. Touching or eating some of the other plants can make you feel sick. A few plants are even more dangerous – they make a poison that is very strong and can kill you. So you should always be careful with plants. Never touch or eat a strange plant – the plant could bite back!

Yew

Canadian woodnettle

Water hemlock

Poison ivy

How do plants sting you? Stinging plants use a special chemical to try to stop animals from eating them. One example of a stinging plant is the poison ivy, which grows all over North America.

The poison ivy has a kind of sticky oil in its leaves and stems. When a person or an animal touches the plant, some of the oil comes out and goes on to their skin. The chemicals in the oil make the sting.

Some people can feel the sting immediately, and usually it is a painful, itchy, or burning feeling. Other people feel nothing at first, and they may not know that they touched the plant. Then, hours later, they start to feel the chemicals working. Their skin turns red, and then blisters (*spots filled with water*) appear. Their skin starts to itch, and it feels terrible. In a few days, the blisters break and liquid comes out. The open blisters (or sores) become hard, and can be there for some time. The sting from a poison ivy certainly looks terrible, and it feels very uncomfortable and painful.

Blisters from poison ivy.

Fruit and nuts
Poison ivy is dangerous, but it has some delicious relatives. Cashew nuts and mango fruit grow on plants of the same family as the poison ivy plant.

The shiny, pointed leaf of the poison ivy plant

So, if you see a poison ivy plant, it is better not to go too near. Animals and people learn to stay away from these stinging plants. But you still may be in danger. You don't have to touch the poison ivy plant itself to get these blisters and sores. The oil from the plant can get onto many different things, for example, other people's clothes, animals, garden tools, balls, or other sports equipment. Then, when you touch these things, the oil gets onto your skin and you start to feel the sting.

The poison ivy has got strong chemicals in its oil, but some other stinging plants have weaker chemicals. This does not mean they are not dangerous – they can be very painful. These plants have to get their poison through the skin to make them work.

The stinging nettle is one kind of plant that can get its poison right through a person's skin. How does it do this? The nettle's sting is a kind of hair. The plant has millions of tiny, sharp spikes (like hairs) on its leaves. If you touch a stinging nettle leaf, some of the spikes will go into your skin. Then the tip of the spike (the part at the end) breaks off, and some poison from inside the spike goes into the skin. The ends of the spikes are very, very sharp, and can cut through skin. And the tips of the spikes break very easily, so the nettle is very good at stinging! When animals like rabbits try to eat the plant, it stings them on the nose and face – they have to learn to stay away, and find some other plant to eat.

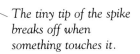

The tiny tip of the spike breaks off when something touches it.

The spike is filled with chemicals (poison).

When the tip breaks off, the end of the spike is sharp enough to cut the skin.

The poison from the stinging nettle usually makes the skin feel painful and itchy, with lots of small, white spots (called a rash). The rash comes on the parts of the skin that touched the plant. Luckily, for most people this rash is not usually serious, and it goes away after an hour or two. But some people may have itchy, painful skin for 24 hours. Like the rabbits, they will remember to stay away from the stinging nettle plant next time!

Help from the dock
The dock plant often grows near nettles. If you break off a dock leaf and hold it on your skin it can help to stop the nettle rash.

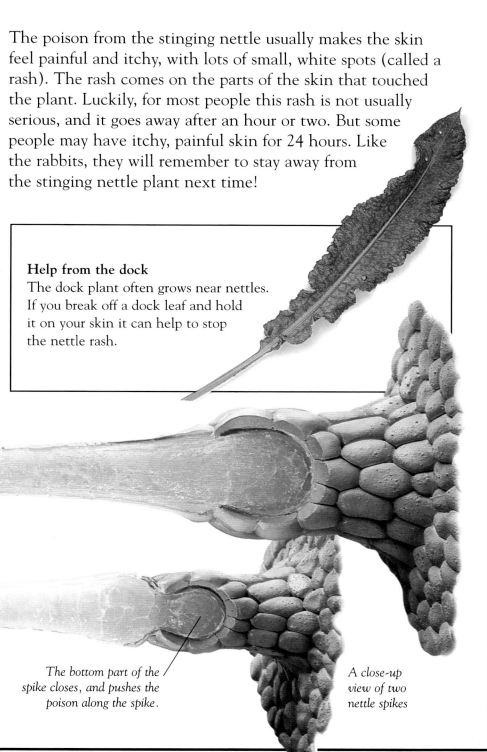

The bottom part of the spike closes, and pushes the poison along the spike.

A close-up view of two nettle spikes

We may not like stinging nettles, or the rash they make on our skin, but nettles are not really dangerous for humans. However, there are some very dangerous stinging plants in the world. The most dangerous are probably the Australian stinger trees – even the name is enough to frighten some people! Anyone travelling in Australia should learn to identify their heart-shaped leaves, and to stay away from them, because these plants can kill. Some stinger trees are like small bushes, but one kind can grow almost 15 metres tall.

    The leaves of the stinger tree are the dangerous parts. Like the stinging nettle, these leaves have lots of tiny hairs all over, like the small hairs on your skin. The hairs have poison inside, and they have very sharp tips. If you touch one of these hairs, the tip of the hair breaks off. Then the plant pushes its poison through the hair and into your skin.

    If you touch a stinger tree only a little with your arm or leg, it will give you a very painful sting – and you should see a doctor or go to hospital. Your arm will be painful for two weeks or more. Scientists don't know all the different chemicals in the poison, and at the moment there is no antidote (something that will stop the poison or illness).

Only one small touch of the stinger tree is painful, but if the plant stings you in a lot of places (for example if you fall on top of it) then you are in real danger. The pain would be very, very bad, and you wouldn't be able to walk or get up. Then more of the leaves could touch your skin. The poison from the plant is very strong, and if a lot of it gets into your body you can die. This plant really is very dangerous, and people have to be very careful when they are near it.

We have looked at plants that trap insects and plants that sting, but many dangerous plants around the world have no traps or stings. Some of these plants are very beautiful. For example, the monkshood in the picture has very pretty blue-purple flowers. It doesn't look dangerous, but it has a very strong poison. The name of this poison is aconitine, and it is deadly – even a tiny amount of this can kill.

People have known about the poison from this plant for a long time – and sometimes they have used it. For example, some people used this poison to kill their enemies hundreds of years ago in Italy. But the person didn't have to eat or drink the poison, so how did it get into their body?

The murderer put some poison from the plant on to a pair of gloves. Then he gave the gloves to his enemy. When the enemy put the gloves on and wore them, the poison was next to their skin. If there were any cuts on the person's fingers, the poison could get into their body. It was a clever way to kill somebody, as it was difficult to catch the murderer!

Wolf killer
Another name for the monkshood plant is "wolf's bane". It got this name because people sometimes used its roots to kill wolves.

The roots, leaves, stems, and even the flowers of the monkshood are poisonous.

Like the monkshood, the prayer bean plant does not look dangerous. It is a pretty plant, with orange flowers and bright red seeds. People have always liked to look at the plant, especially its seeds. In the past in India, some people made the red seeds into necklaces to wear. Because the seeds are all the same size, they make good jewellery. The Indians also made them into special prayer beads for their religion – and so the plant got its name. But this was a problem, because the seeds of the prayer bean plant are very dangerous.

Wearing a necklace made from the prayer beans may look good, but it is a very bad idea. Each little seed looks bright and pretty, but it has enough poison to kill an adult. The seeds are not a problem when they are whole, but if the hard outside skin of the seed is broken, the poison can get out. Then the poison gets on to the person's skin. If there are any small cuts on the skin, the poison gets into the body.

Weighing the seeds
Prayer bean seeds are all the same size and weight. Because of this, people in the past used them to measure the exact weight of other things like gold and diamonds.

Prayer bean plant

When European visitors first went to Malaysia, they heard some strange stories about dangerous plants. One story was very frightening, and that was the story of the deadly upas tree. The Malaysian people said that this tree was called the tree of poisons, and it could kill birds, animals, and people. They said that the upas tree killed the birds flying over it – and the birds did not have to touch the tree. But the most frightening story was about people – they said that anyone who went to sleep under the tree would never wake up.

Now, seven hundred years later, we know that many of these stories are not true. Birds sit on the branches of the upas tree, and nothing happens to them. People can sleep under the tree, and they wake up quite happily. So where did the story about the tree of poisons come from? Was it only a story to frighten the Europeans?

In fact, the upas tree can sometimes be a killer, and it does have a very strong and dangerous poison. The poison is in the sap (*the liquid that comes out if you cut a tree*). If you touch the tree, or cut your skin on the bark (*the hard "skin" or surface of the tree*), you will get a painful rash. If you drink the sap, your heart can stop in a few minutes. So the upas tree really is a deadly killer.

Local people had other ways of using the upas tree in the past. They tied prisoners to the tree, and the poison would slowly go into their skin. In the end the prisoners died. They also put some poison onto a stick, and then killed the prisoner with the stick. Perhaps this is where the stories about never sleeping under the upas tree came from.

This picture from an old book of poisons shows the deadly upas tree.

35

We know that there are thousands of different kinds of plants in the world, and that most of these grow in the tropical rainforests. People use these plants to make many things – for example, medicines. But they also use some more dangerous plants. One example of this is in the Amazon. Deep in the Amazon rainforest, local people have learnt how to make a special poison. It is one of the strongest, most dangerous poisons in the world: curare.

The people of the Amazon rainforest use this poison to hunt animals. The poison is a little bit more difficult to get than the poisons from the upas tree or the prayer bean plant. First, they have to put the bark and roots of a special plant into water, and leave it there for some time. Then they boil the water and it makes a thick liquid, or paste. Now the poison is ready to use.

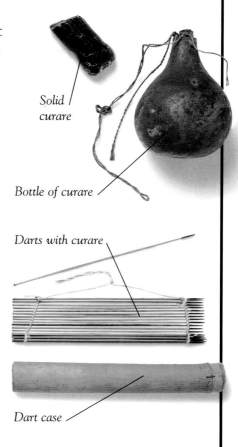

Solid curare

Bottle of curare

Darts with curare

Dart case

A hunter puts some of the paste on the ends of his small darts (*pieces of sharp wood*). He carries the poison darts in a special case. When it is time to hunt, he puts a dart in a blowpipe, then puts the blowpipe up to his mouth. He can blow (or shoot) the dart out of the pipe very fast – like a bullet from a gun.

The special paste is not always strong enough to kill animals, so hunters have to test it. First the hunters shoot their darts at monkeys, to test the poison. If they shoot a monkey and it falls quickly from the tree, they call the poison "one-tree" poison. This is the strongest kind. But if the monkey moves to another tree before falling, then they call it "two-tree" poison. If a monkey moves to a third tree, then the poison is no good, and they don't use it.

Nature's Daggers

Daggers are sharp knives used to kill people, and nature has its own kind of daggers. These are the sharp thorns, spikes, and spines that plants use to protect themselves. Many plants use these "daggers" instead of poison to keep animals and people away, and you can find them almost everywhere in the world. These plants are called "prickly" because it is easy to cut your finger on their sharp spikes – and you can see the spikes on the outside, so they look dangerous!

Bramble

The most prickly of all the plants are the members of the cactus family. You can find them in the deserts (*very dry areas*) of America, from Canada in the north to Chile in the south. Cacti (*the plural of cactus*) don't have any leaves, they have "spines". These sharp spines are very important, because they stop thirsty animals from eating the stem of the cactus. Leaves are not very useful in the desert because they lose water easily.

The stem holds a lot of water, and helps the plant to survive in the dry desert. When there is no water, the stem becomes thin. But when the rain comes, the stem can take in and hold a huge amount of water. The spines also help the plant to take in water. Water falls onto the spines, and then slowly travels down to the roots.

Cactus plants come in all shapes and sizes, but some can grow very tall. The biggest kind of cactus plant is the Saguaro cactus. In 150 years it can grow as big as a five-storey building.

Right: Saguaro cactus

The Mexican "hedgehog" cactus has long, sharp spines like daggers, and they can be very dangerous. A long time ago, the Aztec people of ancient Mexico used the sharp spines of this plant to kill people.

In their religion, the Aztecs sometimes had to make a human sacrifice – this means they had to kill someone and give the person's blood to their gods. When it was time to give human blood to a god, the Aztecs used the hedgehog cactus. They put the bodies of their prisoners on top of the cactus, and the spines cut into their bodies and killed them.

Aztec warriors take prisoners for a human sacrifice on a cactus.

Going fishing?
In the past, people used the strong spines of the "barrel" cactus as hooks to catch fish.

The sharp spines of some cactus plants can be very dangerous, but other cacti cause different problems. They grow groups of strong, fine hairs, and these can be very painful if you touch them. They may not look as bad as the "daggers" of the hedgehog cactus, but after these hairs get into your skin, it is almost impossible to get them out again.

Many people have small plants like these in their homes. They are called "bunny ears" cacti because they look a bit like a rabbit's ears. They are part of the prickly pear family, and have hundreds of hairs all over each stem. But you have to be careful when touching the plants because the hairs can go into the skin.

Prickly pear plants first grew in the Americas, but now they grow in Australia, Africa, and the Mediterranean. Sometimes, these plants grow so well and so quickly that they are a problem to other plants in the area – they cover all the ground.

The stems of this cactus look like a rabbit's ears.

When people think of prickly plants with spines, they usually think of cacti. But another kind of plant with spines is the spurge family. Many people like to have spurge plants in their gardens because they are very pretty, with colourful leaves and flowers.

One popular member of the spurge family is the poinsettia plant. In some countries, people like to have a red and green poinsettia plant in their homes at Christmas time.

Poinsettia

Poinsettia plants in gardens and homes have no sharp spikes. But many wild spurges are spiny and colourful. The sharpest, spikiest example of these wild spurges is the candelabra tree.

The candelabra tree gets its name because of its shape. It looks a bit like a huge candelabra, or candle stand. (A candelabra is something you use to hold a number of candles, all burning at the same time.) But one difference is size: the candelabra we put on the table is quite small, and the candelabra tree is huge!

Look out!
Candelabra tree stems have sap (a milky liquid) that can burn your skin, and if this gets into your eyes it can make you blind.

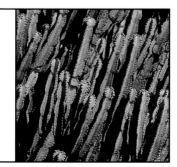

A spiky candelabra tree stem

A candelabra tree growing in Africa.

In South Africa, where candelabra trees grow in the wild, these spurge plants can grow as tall as a house.

The candelabra tree has hundreds of very sharp spikes and a poisonous liquid in its stem. It looks dangerous, and can be very painful. But some people in Africa use this plant to protect their children. If parents have twins (two babies at the same time), they plant two candelabra trees outside their home to mark the birth of their babies. The parents believe that the candelabra trees will protect their children, and stop evil spirits coming near. The parents look after the trees, and everyone can see that there are twins in this house.

Many years later, when the home is gone and the parents and children are dead, you will still see the two trees growing together. Nobody will cut them down.

Controlling the Plants

Of course, plants that have traps, stings, poisons, and spikes – plants that bite back – are not "bad". They have very clever ways of surviving in a difficult world. We human beings may get angry and annoyed at their spikes and stings, but we also know that they can be very useful in many different situations. We have learnt how to use the plants.

Cattle herders (*people who look after the cows*) in some parts of Africa build spiky fences around their cattle to keep the animals safe from hunters. The spikes keep other animals outside, and make the job of the cattle herder easier.

Some people in Mexico also use spiky plants – like the prickly pear cactus – to protect their homes. They plant the cacti as hedges around their gardens to keep thieves out. The thieves know that it is very difficult to climb over the spiky hedge, so when they see the cactus plants, they stay away.

It is not only the spiky plants that are useful to humans – people have also learnt how to use stinging plants like nettles.

Roman soldiers had an unusual use for nettles in winter, when the weather was very cold. The soldiers didn't wear any trousers and their legs and feet could get very cold. So they hit their legs with the nettles, and the sting from the leaves started to work. This made the skin feel warm – the nettle rash was their very strange and clever kind of heating system!

Women also used plants in a strange way – they used them as make-up. One idea was to use a plant with a small sting to make their cheeks red. The women rubbed their cheeks with the leaves of the mullein plant (see the picture below). Mullein leaves have lots of soft, thin hairs, like the leaves of the stinging nettle. These hairs made the skin red, and their cheeks looked bright and healthy. They looked and felt more beautiful!

The spiky cactus plants and the stinging nettle plants can be useful, but what about a poisonous plant? Can a poisonous plant be useful? The answer may surprise you. A large amount of poison from some plants can kill a person, but a small amount of the same poison can cure some illnesses.

One example of this is the poison aconitine, from the deadly monkshood plant. Murderers used this plant to kill their enemies – but it can also cure. Doctors in the past have used small amounts of this poison to help patients who are very nervous. The aconitine helped to make them feel calm.

The foxglove plant (a beautiful, pink flower that grows wild in the countryside and woodlands) has a deadly poison that stops your heart. This plant really is a killer – you could die from heart failure if you ate just four leaves from a foxglove plant. But scientists have studied the chemicals in the plant, and now they can use small amounts of the poison to help people with heart problems.

Foxglove

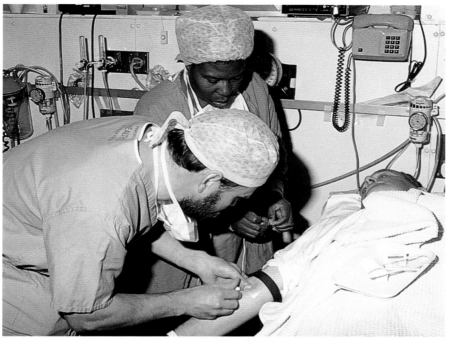

A doctor and nurse give a patient curare before surgery.

Curare is the name of the poisonous chemical used by hunters in the Amazon rainforest. When a poison dart with curare hits an animal, it falls to the ground immediately. It is deadly. But doctors have found a way to use curare in hospitals. In the past they have used it to relax a patient's muscles before taking the patient into the operating theatre for surgery. Another poisonous plant used today is the yew tree. The seeds of the yew tree are inside bright red berries – and they contain a dangerous poison that can kill large animals. Scientists today have learnt how to get special chemicals from the yew tree, and they use these as a drug to help people with cancer.

Yew

47

Glossary

aconitine
A deadly poison in the monkshood plant.

Amazon rainforest
A very wet forest by the Amazon river in South America.

antidote
Something you take to stop the bad effects of a poison.

bait
Something that makes prey come near a trap.

bog, marsh, swamp
Different kinds of soft, wet land.

cactus
A family of plants with sharp spikes and thick stems that hold water.

carnivorous plant
A plant that eats insects and animals.

curare
A poison made from plants, used to hunt animals.

dissolve
Make a solid into a liquid.

fry
Baby fish.

hover
To keep flying in the air in the same place – not going forwards or backwards.

itch
An uncomfortable feeling on the skin – you want to scratch it.

larva
A young animal that looks very different from the adult animal of the same kind.

minerals
Inorganic (not plant or animal) material that all living things need to help them grow.

poison
Something that makes you ill or kills you when you touch or eat it.

prey
Animals that are caught by other animals or plants for food.

rash
A lot of spots on the skin.

spike
Sharp, needle-like part of a plant that can cut your skin.

spine
Sharp points which can hurt you.

sting
Something that makes your skin hot and red when you touch it.

tip
The end or edge of something.

trap
Something that catches insects or animals.

trigger hairs
Hairs that send a message to a plant to start its trap.